Tiny Treasures

Edited By Machaela Gavaghan

First published in Great Britain in 2019 by:

Young Writers
Remus House
Coltsfoot Drive
Peterborough
PE2 9BF
Telephone: 01733 890066
Website: www.youngwriters.co.uk

All Rights Reserved
Book Design by Ashley Janson
© Copyright Contributors 2019
Softback ISBN 978-1-78988-892-8
Hardback ISBN 978-1-83928-470-0
Printed and bound in the UK by BookPrintingUK
Website: www.bookprintinguk.com
YB0418F

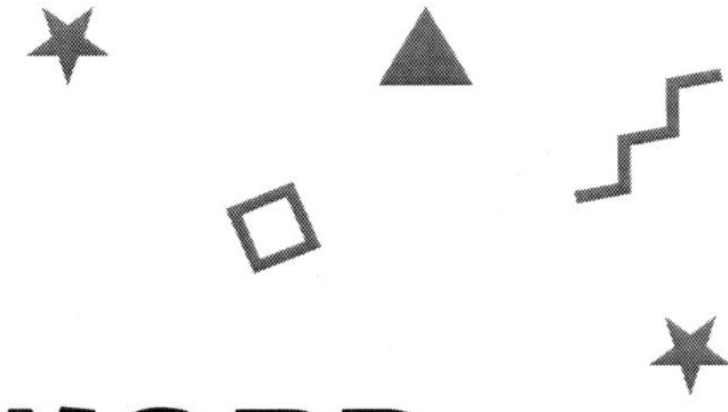

FOREWORD

Dear Reader,

Are you ready to get your thinking caps on to puzzle your way through this wonderful collection?

Young Writers are proud to introduce our new poetry competition, *My First Riddle*, designed to introduce Reception pupils to the delights of poetry. Riddles are a great way to introduce children to the use of poetic expression, including description, similes and expanded noun phrases, as well as encouraging them to 'think outside the box' by providing clues without giving the answer away immediately. Some pupils were given a series of riddle templates to choose from, giving them a framework within which to shape their ideas.

Their answers could be whatever or whoever their imaginations desired; from people to places, animals to objects, food to seasons. All of us here at Young Writers believe in the importance of inspiring young children to produce creative writing, including poetry, and we feel that seeing their own riddles in print will ignite that spark of creativity.

We hope you enjoy riddling your way through this book as much as we enjoyed reading all the entries.

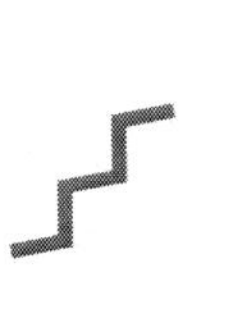

CONTENTS

Independent Entries

Olly Clatworthy (5) 1
Ashika Kajendran (5) 2
Tulsi Shah (5) 3
Jeshua Sam Nicholson (5) 4
Nika Karami (6) 5
Habibah Ghouri (3) 6
Serena Oliveri (6) 7
Daniel James Andrews (4) 8
Iris Pearl Smart (5) 9
Clark Williams (8) 10
Nifemi Sarah Aboyeji (7) 11
Arjun Chotai (6) 12
Muhammad Abdullah (5) 13
Chudi Patrick Onwuokwu 14
Victoria Ooja Okpe 15
Lily Morley (6) 16
Sareena Padayachy 17

Anahilt Primary School, Hillsborough

Holly Shaw (5) 18
Micah Vaughan (5) 19
Daniel Alcorn (5) 20
Elizabeth Houston (5) 21
Maeve Smyth (5) 22

Bonhill Primary School, Bonhill

Sophie Elizabeth Mitchell (5) 23
Caleb Stewart (5) 24
Jake Tolhurst (5) 25
Emelie Hill (5) 26
Elise Gollan (5) 27
Liam Ferguson (5) 28
Ava Ross (5) 29
Sophie Rose Mullen (5) 30
Neve Wallace (5) 31
Cooper Fraser Allison (6) 32
Angus Neave (5) 33
Mia Amy Maxwell (6) 34
Ethan James Duncan Allan (6) 35
Emma Gunn (5) 36
Aimee Sharp (5) 37
Elodie Ferguson (5) 38
Sophia Andrew (6) 39
Kayden Weatherall (5) 40
Zoe McPhail (5) 41
Amy Thompson (6) 42
Maisie Corbett-Dick (5) 43
Connor John Haggerty (6) 44
Amber Niamh Miller (5) 45
Isabella Janet Herd (5) 46
Kyle McKay (5) 47
Noah McGookin (5) 48

Carnlough Controlled Integrated Primary School, Carnlough

Elsa Morrow (6) 49
Clara O'Reilly (5) 50
Annie-Rose Atcheson (6) 51
Olivia Wright-Kerr (6) 52
Scott Reid (5) 53
Olivia Abram (5) 54

Derwent Primary School, Derby

Roxi Ambrose (4) 55
Amelia Paxton (4) 56

Kourtney Marriot (5) 57
Evie-Grace Draper-Tanser (4) 58
Tyler Orme (5) 59
Kathryn Otoole (5) 60
Indianna Ostick (4) 61
Jamie Wheeler (5) 62
Raz Choman (5) 63
Emelia Bea Riviere (5) 64
Layton-Lee Mark Blurton (5) 65
Jamie Lea Gibson (5) 66
Jessica Louise Booth (5) 67
Hannah Hussein (4) 68

Pentland Primary School, Edinburgh

Kelsey Amber Main (8) 69
Sophie Jane Skeldon (8) 70
Elissa Louise Kinghorn (8) 71
Lexie Newcombe (8) 72
Lewis Eric Brunton (8) 73
Caitlin Niamh Healey (8) 74
Tom MacDougall (9) 75
Nieve Bent (9) 76
Viggo Cecchini (9) 77
Yazmin Dow (8) 78
Murray Henry MacGregor (8) 79
Jack Lee (8) 80
Oliver Malcolm (8) 81
Jake Irvine (9) 82

St Anthony's Primary School, Craigavon

Caoimhe Fox (4) 83
Theo James McIlkenny (4) 84
Joanna Urbanska (4) 85
Amelia Corbett (4) 86
Braden Dean O'Hagan (4) 87
Zoey Corbett (4) 88

St Mary's Primary School, Bellaghy

Catherine Diamond (6) 89
Benén Loane (6) 90
Lucia Rose Loane (6) 91
Michael Crozier (6) 92
Aoibheann Scullion (6) 93
Diarmuid McGinn (6) 94
Ellen Lee (6) 95
Aoife McMahon (5) 96
Eunan McLarnon (7) 97
Daniel McAlynn (6) 98
Eimear Scullion (6) 99
Peadár McLarnon (6) 100
Emma Louise Diver (6) 101

Sunnybank Primary School, Aberdeen

Leighton Flores (6) 102
Maria Sereda (5) 103
Marcus Mcgregor (5) 104
Filip Strzelec (5) 105
Denis Cnapic (6) 106
Jaden Gray (5) 107

Thornfield House School, Newtownabbey

Darcey Nicholl (4) 108
Charlie Harrison (6) 109
Tiernan Graffin (5) 110

Waltham St Lawrence Primary School, West End

Ava Williams (5) 111
Chloe Newman (5) 112
Alexandra "Lexy" Elizabeth Barden Gleave (5) 113
Tejas Dholiwar (5) 114

West Heath Primary School, West Heath

Effie Schofield (5) 115
Lashea Shiv Zimmerman (5) 116
Megan Ringham (5) 117
Laila-Rose Kinahan (5) 118
Willow Ford (5) 119
Charlie Skinner (5) 120
Ronnie Marshall (4) 121
Florence Ball (5) 122

Wimbledon Common Preparatory School, Wimbledon

Aarav Sheth (5) 123
Freddy Casey (5) 124
Michael Kok Coustar (5) 125
Matthew Cook (5) 126
Nikolai Gosling (5) 127
James Michael Haywood (5) 128
Noah Thomas (5) 129
Misha Kutsenko (5) 130
Elias Tobler Borsting (5) 131
Johnathan Paice (5) 132
Nathan Zhang (5) 133
David Jeens (5) 134
Frederick Rossen (5) 135
Hugo Stehn (5) 136
L Kee (4) 137
Edward Gleave (5) 138
Henry Michalski (4) 139
Vihaan Narula (5) 140
Jake Collins (5) 141
Pedro Borges Lima (5) 142
Vincent Loganathan (5) 143
Max Lowe (4) 144
Joshua Howard (5) 145
Kabir Malik (5) 146
Atlas Aydin (5) 147
Arlo Mumford (5) 148
Samuel Squelch (5) 149
Hawken Edwards (5) 150
Nicholas Harries (5) 151
Zayne Ali (5) 152
Jack Doran (5) 153

Ysgol Parcyrhun, Ammanford

Arwen Rose Peralta Camanan (5) 154
Parthan Mohan (5) 155

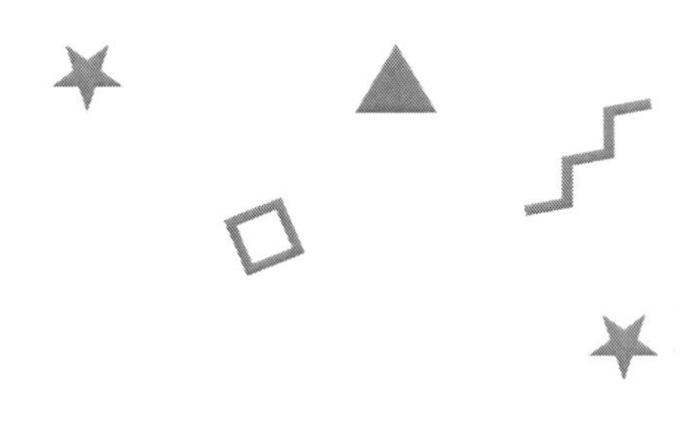

THE RIDDLES

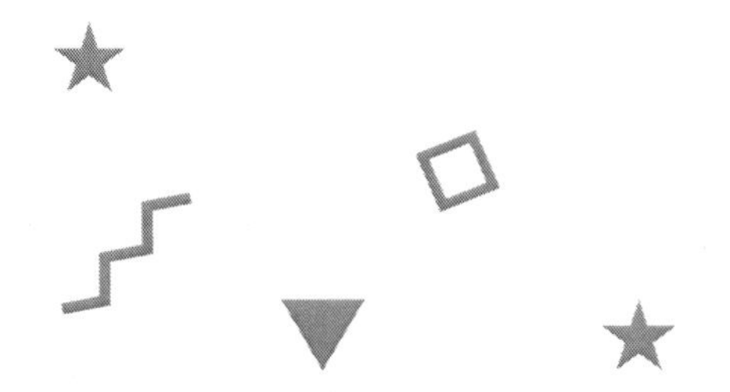

Olly's First Riddle

This is my riddle about an amazing animal.
What could it be?
Follow the clues to see!

This animal has **eight legs** on its body,
And its colour **is yellow, orange and pink.**
This animal has **no** feet,
It likes **snails and slugs** to eat.
The ocean is where it lives,
Its favourite thing to do is **wriggle its legs**.
This animal has **tiny** ears,
It makes **no** sounds for you to hear.

Are you an animal whizz?
Have you guessed what it is?
It is...

Answer: **An octopus.**

Olly Clatworthy (5)

Ashika's First Riddle

This is my riddle about an amazing animal.
What could it be?
Follow the clues to see!

This animal has **fur** on its body,
And its colour is **brown.**
This animal has **four** feet,
It likes **animals** to eat.
Africa is where it lives,
Its favourite thing to do is **rest and hunt.**
This animal has **two** ears,
It makes **roaring** sounds for you to hear.

Are you an animal whizz?
Have you guessed what it is?
It is...

Answer: **A lion.**

Ashika Kajendran (5)

Tulsi's First Riddle

This is my super first riddle.
What could it be?
Follow the clues to see!

With a fairy is where you'll find it,
It's made out of **metal**.
It is used for **magic**,
Its colour is **silver**.
It is a **star** shape,
It has **a stick to hold it with**.

Have you guessed what it could be?
Look below and you will see,
It is...

Answer: **A wand**.

Tulsi Shah (5)

Jeshua's First Riddle

Who could he be?
Follow the clues and see.

He looks **like a big, brown, hairy creature.**
He sounds **like *huff, puff!***
He smells **like burnt hair.**
He feels **like rough hair.**
He tastes **like tough hair.**

Have you guessed who he could be?
Look below and you will see,
He is...

*Answer: **The Big Bad Wolf.***

Jeshua Sam Nicholson (5)

Nika's First Riddle

What could it be?
Follow the clues and see.

It looks **white and sometimes like a rainbow, sometimes a roll or cube shape.**
It sounds **like scratch paper.**
It smells **like chewing gum.**
It feels **soft, like foam and sponge.**
It tastes **like sweet fruit.**

Have you guessed what it could be?
Look below and you will see,
It is...

Answer: **A marshmallow.**

Nika Karami (6)

Habibah's First Riddle

What could it be?
Follow the clues and see.

It looks **like a ball floating in the air.**
It sounds **like a big pop when you poke it.**
It smells **like a pencil rubber.**
It feels **light as a feather.**
It tastes **yucky when you blow it up.**

Have you guessed what it could be?
Look below and you will see,
It is...

Answer: **A balloon.**

Habibah Ghouri (3)

Serena's First Riddle

What could it be?
Follow the clues and see.

It looks like **an apple, but it's not.**
It sounds like **a rolling ball.**
It smells like **a sweet apple.**
It feels like **a soft sponge.**
It tastes like **yummy sweets.**

Have you guessed what it could be?
Look below and you will see,
It is...

Answer: **A peach.**

Serena Oliveri (6)

Daniel's First Riddle

What could it be?
Follow the clues and see.

It looks **white.**
It sounds **like snow.**
It smells **crunchy.**
It feels **like carrots.**
It tastes **like the cold.**

Have you guessed what it could be?
Look below and you will see,
It is...

Answer: **A snowman.**

Daniel James Andrews (4)

Iris' First Riddle

What could it be?
Follow the clues and see.

It looks like **a big snake**.
It sounds like **the wind**.
It smells like **hot fire**.
It feels like **hot wood**.
It tastes like **a barbecue**.

Have you guessed what it could be?
Look below and you will see,
It is...

Answer: **A dragon.**

Iris Pearl Smart (5)

The Seeded Fruit

I have shiny, red skin.
I am hard but smooth to touch.
I am healthy to eat.
I am round like the sun.
I have tiny seeds inside of me.
Take one bite and you could fall asleep for a million years!
What am I?

Answer: A red apple.

Clark Williams (8)

Nifemi's First Riddle

It was bright
There was loads of sunlight
The frogs were jumping
The birds were tweeting
The kids were playing
The grown-ups were watching
The dogs were barking
That's what happens in...

Answer: Summer.

Nifemi Sarah Aboyeji (7)

Arjun's First Riddle

I am not real
I wear blue clothes
I love to play pranks
I have one or two eyes
I wear goggles
I am yellow
What am I?

Answer: A Minion.

Arjun Chotai (6)

Muhammad's First Riddle

It is brown and square
It is soft and sticky
It is gooey like a cookie
It is messy and makes my mouth sticky
What is it?

Answer: A chocolate bar.

Muhammad Abdullah (5)

Chudi's First Riddle

I am a medium-sized creature.
I have a terrible stench.
I have black and white fur.
Some people don't like me.
What am I?

Answer: A skunk.

Chudi Patrick Onwuokwu

Victoria's First Riddle

She is very posh and friendly
She gives you a gentle handshake
She does fun things
Who is she?

Answer: Queen Elizabeth.

Victoria Ooja Okpe

Flowy

I have a bed.
I have a bank.
I never sleep.
I get you wet.
I am fishy.
What am I?

Answer: A river.

Lily Morley (6)

Sareena's First Riddle

I fit into any container,
You can also play a sport in me,
Fire and me are opposites and enemies.

Sareena Padayachy

Holly's First Riddle

What could it be?
Follow the clues and see.

It looks **green, brown and blue.**
It sounds **like flapping wings.**
It smells **like bluebells.**
It feels **rough and bumpy.**
It tastes **wet and cold.**

Have you guessed what it could be?
Look below and you will see,
It is...

Answer: **Hillsborough Forest Park.**

Holly Shaw (5)
Anahilt Primary School, Hillsborough

Micah's First Riddle

What could it be?
Follow the clues and see.

It looks **white, small and cute.**
It sounds **yappy.**
It smells **like a bubble bath.**
It feels **soft and cuddly.**
It tastes **like puppy food.**

Have you guessed what it could be?
Look below and you will see,
It is...

Answer: **My dog, Pippa.**

Micah Vaughan (5)
Anahilt Primary School, Hillsborough

Daniel's First Riddle

What could it be?
Follow the clues and see.

It looks **green and dirty.**
It sounds **noisy.**
It smells **like animals.**
It feels **soft and rough.**
It tastes **like potatoes and vegetables.**

Have you guessed what it could be?
Look below and you will see,
It is...

Answer: **A farm.**

Daniel Alcorn (5)
Anahilt Primary School, Hillsborough

Elizabeth's First Riddle

What could it be?
Follow the clues and see.

It looks **colourful, small and light.**
It sounds **like air.**
It smells **like honey.**
It feels **fragile and delicate.**
It tastes **sweet.**

Have you guessed what it could be?
Look below and you will see,
It is...

Answer: **A butterfly.**

Elizabeth Houston (5)
Anahilt Primary School, Hillsborough

Maeve's First Riddle

What could it be?
Follow the clues and see.

It looks **very high and steep.**
It sounds **peaceful.**
It smells **like sheep and grass.**
It feels **bumpy and cold.**
It tastes **like chocolate.**

Have you guessed what it could be?
Look below and you will see,
It is...

Answer: **A mountain.**

Maeve Smyth (5)

Anahilt Primary School, Hillsborough

Sophie's First Riddle

What could it be?
Follow the clues and see.

It looks **like sprinkles.**
It sounds **like popping.**
It smells **like cotton candy.**
It feels **like little balls.**
It tastes **like bubbles.**

Have you guessed what it could be?
Look below and you will see,
It is...

Answer: **Popping candy.**

Sophie Elizabeth Mitchell (5)
Bonhill Primary School, Bonhill

Caleb's First Riddle

What could it be?
Follow the clues and see.

It looks like **a triangle.**
It sounds **a little bit crunchy.**
It smells **cheesy.**
It feels **hot and soft.**
It tastes **like cheese and tomato.**

Have you guessed what it could be?
Look below and you will see,
It is...

Answer: **A pizza.**

Caleb Stewart (5)
Bonhill Primary School, Bonhill

Jake's First Riddle

What could it be?
Follow the clues and see.

It looks **like a sphere and cone.**
It sounds **yummy.**
It smells **like chocolate.**
It feels **creamy and icy.**
It tastes **cold and yummy.**

Have you guessed what it could be?
Look below and you will see,
It is...

Answer: **Ice cream.**

Jake Tolhurst (5)

Bonhill Primary School, Bonhill

Emelie's First Riddle

What could it be?
Follow the clues and see.

It looks **brown.**
It sounds **crunchy.**
It smells **like cocoa beans.**
It feels **hard.**
It tastes **delicious.**

Have you guessed what it could be?
Look below and you will see,
It is...

Answer: **A bar of chocolate.**

Emelie Hill (5)
Bonhill Primary School, Bonhill

Elise's First Riddle

What could it be?
Follow the clues and see.

It looks **like a brown tower**.
It sounds **squishy**.
It smells **like cheese**.
It feels **soft and squishy**.
It tastes **good and yummy**.

Have you guessed what it could be?
Look below and you will see,
It is...

Answer: **A burger.**

Elise Gollan (5)
Bonhill Primary School, Bonhill

Liam's First Riddle

What could it be?
Follow the clues and see.

It looks **like a ball.**
It sounds **hard when you tap it.**
It smells **sweet**.
It feels **rock-hard**.
It tastes **yummy**.

Have you guessed what it could be?
Look below and you will see,
It is...

Answer: **A jawbreaker.**

Liam Ferguson (5)
Bonhill Primary School, Bonhill

Ava's First Riddle

What could it be?
Follow the clues and see.

It looks **hard.**
It sounds **crinkly.**
It smells **sweet.**
It feels **like popping.**
It tastes **like sweet bubblegum.**

Have you guessed what it could be?
Look below and you will see,
It is...

Answer: **Popping candy.**

Ava Ross (5)
Bonhill Primary School, Bonhill

Sophie's First Riddle

What could it be?
Follow the clues and see.

It looks **swirly.**
It sounds **drippy.**
It smells **like strawberries.**
It feels **soft and cold.**
It tastes **creamy and wet.**

Have you guessed what it could be?
Look below and you will see,
It is...

Answer: **Ice cream.**

Sophie Rose Mullen (5)
Bonhill Primary School, Bonhill

Neve's First Riddle

What could it be?
Follow the clues and see.

It looks **red and round**.
It sounds **crunchy when you bite it**.
It smells **sweet**.
It feels **hard**.
It tastes **juicy**.

Have you guessed what it could be?
Look below and you will see,
It is...

Answer: **An apple.**

Neve Wallace (5)
Bonhill Primary School, Bonhill

Cooper's First Riddle

What could it be?
Follow the clues and see.

It looks **like a circle.**
It sounds **soft when you eat it.**
It smells **delicious.**
It feels **soft.**
It tastes **cheesy.**

Have you guessed what it could be?
Look below and you will see,
It is...

Answer: **A pizza.**

Cooper Fraser Allison (6)
Bonhill Primary School, Bonhill

Angus' First Riddle

What could it be?
Follow the clues and see.

It looks **green.**
It sounds **crunchy.**
It smells **like sweet juice.**
It feels **hard and soft.**
It tastes **juicy and sweet.**

Have you guessed what it could be?
Look below and you will see,
It is...

Answer: **An apple.**

Angus Neave (5)
Bonhill Primary School, Bonhill

Mia's First Riddle

What could it be?
Follow the clues and see.

It looks **sticky.**
It sounds **hard when you tap it.**
It smells **sweet.**
It feels **soft inside.**
It tastes **yummy.**

Have you guessed what it could be?
Look below and you will see,
It is...

Answer: **A lollipop.**

Mia Amy Maxwell (6)
Bonhill Primary School, Bonhill

Ethan's First Riddle

What could it be?
Follow the clues and see.

It looks **like a cloud**.
It sounds **drippy**.
It smells **like vanilla.**
It feels **soft.**
It tastes **sweet and wet.**

Have you guessed what it could be?
Look below and you will see,
It is...

Answer: **Ice cream.**

Ethan James Duncan Allan (6)
Bonhill Primary School, Bonhill

Emma's First Riddle

What could it be?
Follow the clues and see.

It looks **white and tall.**
It sounds **cold**.
It smells **nice and creamy**.
It feels **hard**.
It tastes **like chocolate**.

Have you guessed what it could be?
Look below and you will see,
It is...

Answer: **Ice cream.**

Emma Gunn (5)
Bonhill Primary School, Bonhill

Aimee's First Riddle

What could it be?
Follow the clues and see.

It looks **like a circle**.
It sounds **smooth**.
It smells **like bubblegum**.
It feels **cold and soft**.
It tastes **yummy**.

Have you guessed what it could be?
Look below and you will see,
It is...

Answer: **Ice cream**.

Aimee Sharp (5)
Bonhill Primary School, Bonhill

Elodie's First Riddle

What could it be?
Follow the clues and see.

It looks **red.**
It sounds **crunchy when you bite it.**
It smells **yummy.**
It feels **hard.**
It tastes **sweet.**

Have you guessed what it could be?
Look below and you will see,
It is...

Answer: **A strawberry.**

Elodie Ferguson (5)
Bonhill Primary School, Bonhill

Sophia's First Riddle

What could it be?
Follow the clues and see.

It looks **yellow**.
It sounds **hard when you tap it.**
It smells **sour**.
It feels **soft inside.**
It tastes **nice.**

Have you guessed what it could be?
Look below and you will see,
It is...

Answer: **A lemon.**

Sophia Andrew (6)
Bonhill Primary School, Bonhill

Kayden's First Riddle

What could it be?
Follow the clues and see.

It looks **black.**
It sounds **bubbly.**
It smells **nice.**
It feels **wet.**
It tastes **like cola bottles.**

Have you guessed what it could be?
Look below and you will see,
It is...

Answer: **A glass of fizzy juice.**

Kayden Weatherall (5)
Bonhill Primary School, Bonhill

Zoe's First Riddle

What could it be?
Follow the clues and see.

It looks **like ice.**
It sounds **watery.**
It smells **like raspberries.**
It feels **freezing.**
It tastes **yummy.**

Have you guessed what it could be?
Look below and you will see,
It is...

Answer: **A Slush Puppie.**

Zoe McPhail (5)
Bonhill Primary School, Bonhill

Amy's First Riddle

What could it be?
Follow the clues and see.

It looks **like a sphere**.
It sounds **crunchy**.
It smells **sweet**.
It feels **hard**.
It tastes **crunchy and nice**.

Have you guessed what it could be?
Look below and you will see,
It is...

Answer: **An apple**.

Amy Thompson (6)
Bonhill Primary School, Bonhill

Maisie's First Riddle

What could it be?
Follow the clues and see.

It looks **like a triangle**.
It sounds **soft**.
It smells **cheesy**.
It feels **squishy**.
It tastes **good**.

Have you guessed what it could be?
Look below and you will see,
It is...

Answer: **A pizza.**

Maisie Corbett-Dick (5)
Bonhill Primary School, Bonhill

Connor's First Riddle

What could it be?
Follow the clues and see.

It looks **yellow and round.**
It sounds **crunchy**.
It smells **salty**.
It feels **jagged**.
It tastes **good**.

Have you guessed what it could be?
Look below and you will see,
It is...

Answer: **A crisp**.

Connor John Haggerty (6)
Bonhill Primary School, Bonhill

Amber's First Riddle

What could it be?
Follow the clues and see.

It looks **blue**.
It sounds **hard**.
It smells **sweet**.
It feels **sticky**.
It tastes **delicious**.

Have you guessed what it could be?
Look below and you will see,
It is...

Answer: **Bubblegum**.

Amber Niamh Miller (5)
Bonhill Primary School, Bonhill

Isabella's First Riddle

What could it be?
Follow the clues and see.

It looks **hard**.
It sounds **crunchy**.
It smells **sweet**.
It feels **smooth**.
It tastes **juicy**.

Have you guessed what it could be?
Look below and you will see,
It is...

Answer: **An apple.**

Isabella Janet Herd (5)
Bonhill Primary School, Bonhill

Kyle's First Riddle

What could it be?
Follow the clues and see.

It looks **blue**.
It sounds **fluffy**.
It smells **sweet**.
It feels **soft**.
It tastes **yummy**.

Have you guessed what it could be?
Look below and you will see,
It is...

Answer: **Candyfloss**.

Kyle McKay (5)

Bonhill Primary School, Bonhill

Noah's First Riddle

What could it be?
Follow the clues and see.

It looks **red**.
It sounds **crunchy**.
It smells **good**.
It feels **cold**.
It tastes **wet**.

Have you guessed what it could be?
Look below and you will see,
It is...

Answer: **A Slush Puppie.**

Noah McGookin (5)
Bonhill Primary School, Bonhill

Elsa's First Riddle

What could it be?
Follow the clues and see.

It looks **brown and hairy**.
It sounds **like *oo, oo, ah, ah***.
It smells **like dust**.
It feels **soft**.
It tastes **like a banana**.

Have you guessed what it could be?
Look below and you will see,
It is...

Answer: **A monkey.**

Elsa Morrow (6)
Carnlough Controlled Integrated Primary School, Carnlough

Clara's First Riddle

What could it be?
Follow the clues and see.

It looks **black and white.**
It sounds **gentle and quiet.**
It smells **like the wild.**
It feels **smooth.**
It tastes **like fresh grass.**

Have you guessed what it could be?
Look below and you will see,
It is...

Answer: **A zebra.**

Clara O'Reilly (5)
Carnlough Controlled Integrated Primary School, Carnlough

Annie-Rose's First Riddle

What could it be?
Follow the clues and see.

It looks **large and grey**.
It sounds **like feet stomping**.
It smells **of fresh water**.
It feels **rough**.
It tastes **like fruit**.

Have you guessed what it could be?
Look below and you will see,
It is...

Answer: **An elephant.**

Annie-Rose Atcheson (6)
Carnlough Controlled Integrated Primary School, Carnlough

Olivia's First Riddle

What could it be?
Follow the clues and see.

It looks **yellow and spotty.**
It sounds **like a race car.**
It smells **of its dinner.**
It feels **smooth.**
It tastes **like meat.**

Have you guessed what it could be?
Look below and you will see,
It is...

Answer: **A cheetah.**

Olivia Wright-Kerr (6)
Carnlough Controlled Integrated Primary School, Carnlough

Scott's First Riddle

What could it be?
Follow the clues and see.

It looks **strong and furry**.
It sounds **like *roar!***
It smells **musky**.
It feels **furry**.
It tastes **bitter**.

Have you guessed what it could be?
Look below and you will see,
It is...

Answer: **A lion.**

Scott Reid (5)
Carnlough Controlled Integrated Primary School,
Carnlough

Olivia's First Riddle

What could it be?
Follow the clues and see.

It looks **stripy and orange**.
It sounds **scary**.
It smells **stinky**.
It feels **soft**.
It tastes **like meat**.

Have you guessed what it could be?
Look below and you will see,
It is...

Answer: **A tiger**.

Olivia Abram (5)
Carnlough Controlled Integrated Primary School, Carnlough

Roxi's First Riddle

What could it be?
Follow the clues and see.

It looks **like a rainbow.**
It sounds **like *clippety-clop*.**
It smells **like cotton candy.**
It feels **soft and smooth.**
It tastes **like magic.**

Have you guessed what it could be?
Look below and you will see,
It is...

Answer: **A unicorn.**

Roxi Ambrose (4)
Derwent Primary School, Derby

Amelia's First Riddle

What could it be?
Follow the clues and see.

It looks **brown and furry**.
It sounds **like *oo, oo, ah, ah*.**
It smells **like banana**.
It feels **soft and fluffy**.
It tastes **like banana**.

Have you guessed what it could be?
Look below and you will see,
It is...

Answer: **A monkey.**

Amelia Paxton (4)
Derwent Primary School, Derby

Kourtney's First Riddle

What could it be?
Follow the clues and see.

It looks **cute and jumpy**.
It sounds **like *boing, boing***.
It smells **lovely**.
It feels **soft and cuddly**.
It tastes **like carrots**.

Have you guessed what it could be?
Look below and you will see,
It is...

Answer: **A rabbit.**

Kourtney Marriot (5)
Derwent Primary School, Derby

Evie-Grace's First Riddle

What could it be?
Follow the clues and see.

It looks **brown and shiny.**
It sounds **swishy.**
It smells **like grass and hay.**
It feels **soft and smooth.**
It tastes **like a carrot.**

Have you guessed what it could be?
Look below and you will see,
It is...

Answer: **A horse.**

Evie-Grace Draper-Tanser (4)
Derwent Primary School, Derby

Tyler's First Riddle

What could it be?
Follow the clues and see.

It looks **happy and cheeky.**
It sounds **noisy.**
It smells **stinky and yucky.**
It feels **furry and soft.**
It tastes **like banana.**

Have you guessed what it could be?
Look below and you will see,
It is...

Answer: **A monkey.**

Tyler Orme (5)
Derwent Primary School, Derby

Kathryn's First Riddle

What could it be?
Follow the clues and see.

It looks **huge and grey**.
It sounds **stompy and loud**.
It smells **stinky**.
It feels **freckly**.
It tastes **like water**.

Have you guessed what it could be?
Look below and you will see,
It is...

Answer: **An elephant**.

Kathryn Otoole (5)
Derwent Primary School, Derby

Indianna's First Riddle

What could it be?
Follow the clues and see.

It looks **colourful.**
It sounds **like animals.**
It smells **like lots of trees.**
It feels **sunny.**
It tastes **like oranges.**

Have you guessed what it could be?
Look below and you will see,
It is...

Answer: **The jungle.**

Indianna Ostick (4)
Derwent Primary School, Derby

Jamie's First Riddle

What could it be?
Follow the clues and see.

It looks **orange and golden**.
It sounds **bubbly and quiet**.
It smells **like a peach**.
It feels **wet**.
It tastes **fishy**.

Have you guessed what it could be?
Look below and you will see,
It is...

Answer: **A fish.**

Jamie Wheeler (5)
Derwent Primary School, Derby

Raz's First Riddle

What could it be?
Follow the clues and see.

It looks **black and fat.**
It sounds **like *meow*.**
It smells **good.**
It feels **soft and furry.**
It tastes **like milk.**

Have you guessed what it could be?
Look below and you will see,
It is...

Answer: **A cat.**

Raz Choman (5)
Derwent Primary School, Derby

Emelia's First Riddle

What could it be?
Follow the clues and see.

It looks **silver.**
It sounds **nibbly.**
It smells **like straw.**
It feels **soft and fluffy.**
It tastes **like carrots.**

Have you guessed what it could be?
Look below and you will see,
It is...

Answer: **A rabbit.**

Emelia Bea Riviere (5)
Derwent Primary School, Derby

Layton-Lee's First Riddle

What could it be?
Follow the clues and see.

It looks **fierce and hungry.**
It sounds **noisy**.
It smells **like the jungle**.
It feels **soft and furry**.
It tastes **yummy**.

Have you guessed what it could be?
Look below and you will see,
It is...

Answer: **A lion.**

Layton-Lee Mark Blurton (5)
Derwent Primary School, Derby

Jamie-Lea's First Riddle

What could it be?
Follow the clues and see.

It looks **busy**.
It sounds **noisy and loud**.
It smells **like food**.
It feels **like people**.
It tastes **like sausages**.

Have you guessed what it could be?
Look below and you will see,
It is...

Answer: **Town**.

Jamie Lea Gibson (5)
Derwent Primary School, Derby

Jessica's First Riddle

What could it be?
Follow the clues and see.

It looks **big and grey**.
It sounds **loud**.
It smells **like poop**.
It feels **hairy**.
It tastes **like bananas**.

Have you guessed what it could be?
Look below and you will see,
It is...

Answer: **An elephant.**

Jessica Louise Booth (5)
Derwent Primary School, Derby

Hannah's First Riddle

What could it be?
Follow the clues and see.

It looks **brown**.
It sounds **neigh-y**.
It smells **like straw**.
It feels **soft**.
It tastes **like straw**.

Have you guessed what it could be?
Look below and you will see,
It is...

Answer: **A horse**.

Hannah Hussein (4)
Derwent Primary School, Derby

Kelsey's First Riddle

What could it be?
Follow the clues and see.

It looks **white pieces of snow dripping down.**
It sounds **like shimmering golden bells ringing from a big tower.**
It smells **like swishy hot chocolate and cookies being baked.**
It feels **chilly, your toes and fingers freeze up.**
It tastes **like a burning hot drink with soft marshmallows.**

Have you guessed what it could be?
Look below and you will see,
It is...

Answer: **Winter.**

Kelsey Amber Main (8)
Pentland Primary School, Edinburgh

Sophie's First Riddle

What could it be?
Follow the clues and see.

It looks **like a big, grey, rainy day.**
It sounds **like a trumpet tooting a high note.**
It smells **like the sweet smell of berries in the rainforest.**
It feels **like scary snakes slithering to form a curious shape.**
It tastes **like fresh water sprinkling all over me.**

Have you guessed what it could be?
Look below and you will see,
It is...

Answer: **An elephant.**

Sophie Jane Skeldon (8)
Pentland Primary School, Edinburgh

Elissa's First Riddle

What could it be?
Follow the clues and see.

It looks **like it is very green.**
It sounds **like something being cut, very beautiful and green.**
It smells **fresh when it's been cut, very amazing.**
It feels **soft and nice, like a tree.**
It tastes **like a leaf but you won't want to taste it.**

Have you guessed what it could be?
Look below and you will see,
It is...

Answer: **Grass.**

Elissa Louise Kinghorn (8)
Pentland Primary School, Edinburgh

Lexie's First Riddle

What could it be?
Follow the clues and see.

It looks **like the beach with kids having fun.**
It sounds **like the roaring waves of the sea.**
It smells **like the sea shimmering in the distance.**
It feels **like the warm sand on my toes.**
It tastes **like a refreshing drink cooling me down.**

Have you guessed what it could be?
Look below and you will see,
It is...

Answer: **A holiday.**

Lexie Newcombe (8)
Pentland Primary School, Edinburgh

Lewis' First Riddle

What could it be?
Follow the clues and see.

It looks **a big kid with a messy face.**
It sounds **like a kid crying after he's dropped his new toy.**
It smells **like milk and a lot of lovely sugar.**
It feels **like sticky hands and wet legs.**
It tastes **like strawberry goodness!**

Have you guessed what it could be?
Look below and you will see,
It is...

Answer: **Ice cream.**

Lewis Eric Brunton (8)
Pentland Primary School, Edinburgh

Caitlin's First Riddle

What could it be?
Follow the clues and see.

It looks **like blue, big, sparkling waves in the sun.**
It sounds **like whistling waves.**
It smells **like fresh, clean water.**
It feels **like wet, cold water on my body.**
It tastes **like yucky, salty water.**

Have you guessed what it could be?
Look below and you will see,
It is...

Answer: **The sea.**

Caitlin Niamh Healey (8)
Pentland Primary School, Edinburgh

Tom's First Riddle

What could it be?
Follow the clues and see.

It looks **like disgusting bogies.**
It sounds **like grass swaying in the wind.**
It smells **like the sweet spring grass.**
It feels **like soft, spiky leaves.**
It tastes **like warm peas that have just come out of the oven.**

Have you guessed what it could be?
Look below and you will see,
It is...

Answer: **The colour green.**

Tom MacDougall (9)
Pentland Primary School, Edinburgh

Nieve's First Riddle

What could it be?
Follow the clues and see.

It looks **like a big, huge eye coming out.**
It sounds **like the whistling wind blowing on me.**
It smells **like the beautiful waves.**
It feels **like the sun is beaming on me.**
It tastes **like ice cream dripping from the sky.**

Have you guessed what it could be?
Look below and you will see,
It is...

Answer: **The sea.**

Nieve Bent (9)
Pentland Primary School, Edinburgh

Viggo's First Riddle

What could it be?
Follow the clues and see.

It looks **like an eagle swooping in the sky.**
It sounds **like a dog whimpering sadly.**
It smells **like nature in the sun.**
It feels **like feathers on my finger.**
It tastes **like chicken in the hot oven.**

Have you guessed what it could be?
Look below and you will see,
It is...

Answer: **A barn owl.**

Viggo Cecchini (9)
Pentland Primary School, Edinburgh

Yazmin's First Riddle

What could it be?
Follow the clues and see.

It looks **green on the hills as it whistles in the wind.**
It sounds **loud and adorable because of the animals.**
It smells **fresh and bitter.**
It feels **soft and fluffy.**
It tastes **so yummy and fresh.**

Have you guessed what it could be?
Look below and you will see,
It is...

Answer: **Spring.**

Yazmin Dow (8)
Pentland Primary School, Edinburgh

Murray's First Riddle

What could it be?
Follow the clues and see.

It looks **like very scary costumes.**
It sounds **like wolves howling in the wind.**
It smells **of the night becoming dawn.**
It feels **like the winding of a clock.**
It tastes **like sweets.**

Have you guessed what it could be?
Look below and you will see,
It is...

Answer: **Halloween.**

Murray Henry MacGregor (8)
Pentland Primary School, Edinburgh

Jack's First Riddle

What could it be?
Follow the clues and see.

It looks **like an ugly monster.**
It sounds **like kids laughing.**
It smells **like a nice, strong, sweet smell.**
It feels **like the wind blowing past me.**
It tastes **like chocolate and sweets.**

Have you guessed what it could be?
Look below and you will see,
It is...

Answer: **Halloween.**

Jack Lee (8)
Pentland Primary School, Edinburgh

Oliver's First Riddle

What could it be?
Follow the clues and see.

It looks **busy**.
It sounds **like a herd of elephants.**
It smells **like air**.
It feels **smooth or bumpy**.
It tastes **so very horrible.**

Have you guessed what it could be?
Look below and you will see,
It is...

Answer: **A classroom.**

Oliver Malcolm (8)
Pentland Primary School, Edinburgh

Jake's First Riddle

What could it be?
Follow the clues and see.

It looks **like a tree falling down**.
It sounds **like bells**.
It smells **like a shoe**.
It feels **cold**.
It tastes **like turkey**.

Have you guessed what it could be?
Look below and you will see,
It is...

Answer: **Christmas.**

Jake Irvine (9)
Pentland Primary School, Edinburgh

Caoimhe's First Riddle

What could it be?
Follow the clues and see.

It looks **like mini yellow clouds**.
It sounds **like *pop, pop, pop* or *crunch, crunch, crunch***.
It smells **salty, sweet or buttery**.
It feels **soft, squishy and warm.**
It tastes **delicious, salty or sweet.**

Have you guessed what it could be?
Look below and you will see,
It is...

Answer: **Popcorn.**

Caoimhe Fox (4)

St Anthony's Primary School, Craigavon

Theo's First Riddle

What could it be?
Follow the clues and see.

It looks **brown and tall.**
It sounds **like little whispers.**
It smells **like fresh air.**
It feels **hard, like rocks.**
It tastes **sweet like apples.**

Have you guessed what it could be?
Look below and you will see,
It is...

Answer: **A tree in spring.**

Theo James McIlkenny (4)
St Anthony's Primary School, Craigavon

Joanna's First Riddle

What could it be?
Follow the clues and see.

It looks **brown and rectangular.**
It sounds **crunchy and chewy.**
It smells **sweet and heavenly.**
It feels **soft and melty.**
It tastes **delicious.**

Have you guessed what it could be?
Look below and you will see,
It is...

Answer: Chocolate.

Joanna Urbanska (4)
St Anthony's Primary School, Craigavon

Amelia's First Riddle

What could it be?
Follow the clues and see.

It looks **like a circle**.
It sounds **like *tick-tock***.
It smells **like wood**.
It feels **hard and smooth**.
It tastes **yucky**.

Have you guessed what it could be?
Look below and you will see,
It is...

Answer: **A clock**.

Amelia Corbett (4)
St Anthony's Primary School, Craigavon

Braden's First Riddle

What could it be?
Follow the clues and see.

It looks **round and green.**
It sounds **juicy**.
It smells **sweet**.
It feels **smooth**.
It tastes **crunchy**.

Have you guessed what it could be?
Look below and you will see,
It is...

Answer: **A green apple.**

Braden Dean O'Hagan (4)
St Anthony's Primary School, Craigavon

Zoey's First Riddle

What could it be?
Follow the clues and see.

It looks **colourful**.
It sounds **peaceful**.
It smells **beautiful**.
It feels **soft**.
It tastes **yucky**.

Have you guessed what it could be?
Look below and you will see,
It is...

Answer: **A flower.**

Zoey Corbett (4)
St Anthony's Primary School, Craigavon

Catherine's First Riddle

What could it be?
Follow the clues and see.

It looks **sprinkly.**
It sounds **like the ice cream van's music.**
It smells **tasty and yummy.**
It feels **like a soft snowman.**
It tastes **like vanilla.**

Have you guessed what it could be?
Look below and you will see,
It is...

Answer: **Ice cream.**

Catherine Diamond (6)
St Mary's Primary School, Bellaghy

Benén's First Riddle

What could it be?
Follow the clues and see.

It looks **orange or red**.
It sounds **like *bing, bing, bing.***
It smells **like the ocean**.
It feels **stingy**.
It tastes **wibbly-wobbly**.

Have you guessed what it could be?
Look below and you will see,
It is...

Answer: ***A jellyfish.***

Benén Loane (6)
St Mary's Primary School, Bellaghy

Lucia Rose's First Riddle

What could it be?
Follow the clues and see.

It looks **long with a wavy tail.**
It sounds **like a hummingbird.**
It smells **like flowers.**
It feels **smooth and scaly.**
It tastes **sandy and salty.**

Have you guessed what it could be?
Look below and you will see,
It is...

Answer: **A mermaid.**

Lucia Rose Loane (6)
St Mary's Primary School, Bellaghy

Michael's First Riddle

What could it be?
Follow the clues and see.

It looks **orange and red.**
It sounds **like *clickety-clack.***
It smells **like the sea.**
It feels **sharp and prickly.**
It tastes **crunchy.**

Have you guessed what it could be?
Look below and you will see,
It is...

Answer: **A crab.**

Michael Crozier (6)
St Mary's Primary School, Bellaghy

Aoibheann's First Riddle

What could it be?
Follow the clues and see.

It looks **blue and yellow.**
It sounds **like it can talk.**
It smells **like the sea.**
It feels **like its tail is scaly.**
It tastes **slimy and crunchy.**

Have you guessed what it could be?
Look below and you will see,
It is...

Answer: **A mermaid.**

Aoibheann Scullion (6)
St Mary's Primary School, Bellaghy

Diarmuid's First Riddle

What could it be?
Follow the clues and see.

It looks **blue and clear.**
It sounds **like noisy seagulls.**
It smells **like bubblegum ice cream.**
It feels **sandy and warm.**
It tastes **salty.**

Have you guessed what it could be?
Look below and you will see,
It is...

Answer: **The seaside.**

Diarmuid McGinn (6)
St Mary's Primary School, Bellaghy

Ellen's First Riddle

What could it be?
Follow the clues and see.

It looks **glittery and blue.**
It sounds **loud and squeaky.**
It smells **like the sea.**
It feels **soft and pink.**
It tastes **like sand.**

Have you guessed what it could be?
Look below and you will see,
It is...

Answer: **A dolphin.**

Ellen Lee (6)
St Mary's Primary School, Bellaghy

Aoife's First Riddle

What could it be?
Follow the clues and see.

It looks **white and orange.**
It sounds **like it is blowing bubbles.**
It smells **fishy.**
It feels **nice and cold.**
It tastes **fishy.**

Have you guessed what it could be?
Look below and you will see,
It is...

Answer: **A clownfish.**

Aoife McMahon (5)
St Mary's Primary School, Bellaghy

Eunan's First Riddle

What could it be?
Follow the clues and see.

It looks **colourful**.
It sounds **quiet and peaceful**.
It smells **like Mummy's dinner**.
It feels **slimy**.
It tastes **so good**.

Have you guessed what it could be?
Look below and you will see,
It is...

Answer: **A fish.**

Eunan McLarnon (7)
St Mary's Primary School, Bellaghy

Daniel's First Riddle

What could it be?
Follow the clues and see.

It looks **big and wet.**
It sounds **quiet.**
It smells **like strawberry jelly**.
It feels **weird.**
It tastes **spongy and soft.**

Have you guessed what it could be?
Look below and you will see,
It is...

Answer: **A jellyfish.**

Daniel McAlynn (6)
St Mary's Primary School, Bellaghy

Eimear's First Riddle

What could it be?
Follow the clues and see.

It looks **very blue**.
It sounds **wavy**.
It smells **like goldfish**.
It feels **wet and salty**.
It tastes **salty, like my chips**.

Have you guessed what it could be?
Look below and you will see,
It is...

Answer: **The sea.**

Eimear Scullion (6)
St Mary's Primary School, Bellaghy

Peadár's First Riddle

What could it be?
Follow the clues and see.

It looks **dark blue.**
It sounds **like the sea.**
It smells **like fish.**
It feels **wet.**
It tastes **like sugar and sweets.**

Have you guessed what it could be?
Look below and you will see,
It is...

Answer: **Water.**

Peadár McLarnon (6)
St Mary's Primary School, Bellaghy

Emma's First Riddle

What could it be?
Follow the clues and see.

It looks **sandy**.
It sounds **very noisy**.
It smells **salty**.
It feels **soft**.
It tastes **like ice cream**.

Have you guessed what it could be?
Look below and you will see,
It is...

Answer: **The beach.**

Emma Louise Diver (6)
St Mary's Primary School, Bellaghy

Leighton's First Riddle

What could it be?
Follow the clues and see.

It looks **like two circles with legs.**
It sounds **creaky sometimes.**
It smells **like metal.**
It feels **hard.**
It tastes **cold.**

Have you guessed what it could be?
Look below and you will see,
It is...

Answer: **Glasses.**

Leighton Flores (6)
Sunnybank Primary School, Aberdeen

Maria's First Riddle

What could it be?
Follow the clues and see.

It looks **brown and round**.
It sounds **quiet**.
It smells **like a sponge**.
It feels **sweet**.
It tastes **yummy**.

Have you guessed what it could be?
Look below and you will see,
It is...

Answer: **A chocolate cake.**

Maria Sereda (5)
Sunnybank Primary School, Aberdeen

Marcus' First Riddle

What could it be?
Follow the clues and see.

It looks **brown and fluffy**.
It sounds **loud**.
It smells **not nice in the water**.
It feels **soft**.
It tastes **not nice**.

Have you guessed what it could be?
Look below and you will see,
It is...

Answer: **A dog**.

Marcus Mcgregor (5)
Sunnybank Primary School, Aberdeen

Filip's First Riddle

What could it be?
Follow the clues and see.

It looks **like a green rectangle.**
It sounds **like paper.**
It smells **old.**
It feels **smooth.**
We should not eat it.

Have you guessed what it could be?
Look below and you will see,
It is...

Answer: **Money.**

Filip Strzelec (5)
Sunnybank Primary School, Aberdeen

Denis' First Riddle

What could it be?
Follow the clues and see.

It looks **yellow**.
It sounds **like a tear**.
It smells **fruity**.
It feels **smooth**.
It tastes **soft**.

Have you guessed what it could be?
Look below and you will see,
It is...

Answer: **A banana.**

Denis Cnapic (6)
Sunnybank Primary School, Aberdeen

Jaden's First Riddle

What could it be?
Follow the clues and see.

It looks **yellow**.
It sounds **loud**.
It smells **fluffy**.
It feels **like nature**.
It tastes **furry**.

Have you guessed what it could be?
Look below and you will see,
It is...

Answer: **A lion.**

Jaden Gray (5)
Sunnybank Primary School, Aberdeen

Darcey's First Riddle

What could it be?
Follow the clues and see.

It looks **like lots of fun.**
It sounds **like music and giggles.**
It smells **like cakes and goodies.**
It feels **like happiness and friends.**
It tastes **like sweets and treats.**

Have you guessed what it could be?
Look below and you will see,
It is...

Answer: **A party.**

Darcey Nicholl (4)
Thornfield House School, Newtownabbey

Charlie's First Riddle

What could it be?
Follow the clues and see.

It looks **black and has four legs.**
It sounds **like** ***grr*****.**
It smells **stinky**.
It feels **furry.**
It tastes **yucky**.

Have you guessed what it could be?
Look below and you will see,
It is...

Answer: **A black panther.**

Charlie Harrison (6)
Thornfield House School, Newtownabbey

Tiernan's First Riddle

What could it be?
Follow the clues and see.

It looks **like a rainbow.**
It sounds **like nothing.**
It smells **like fruit.**
It feels **cold.**
It tastes **yummy.**

Have you guessed what it could be?
Look below and you will see,
It is...

Answer: **An ice lolly.**

Tiernan Graffin (5)
Thornfield House School, Newtownabbey

Ava's First Riddle

What could it be?
Follow the clues and see.

It looks **colourful and fluffy**.
It sounds **like *neigh, neigh*.**
It smells **like a rose**.
It feels **soft**.
It tastes **like sweeties**.

Have you guessed what it could be?
Look below and you will see,
It is...

Answer: **A unicorn.**

Ava Williams (5)

Waltham St Lawrence Primary School, West End

Chloe's First Riddle

What could it be?
Follow the clues and see.

It looks **like ice**.
It sounds **like, "Hi."**
It smells **with its carrot on its nose**.
It feels **cold, like ice cream**.
It tastes **like ice cream**.

Have you guessed what it could be?
Look below and you will see,
It is...

Answer: **A snowman.**

Chloe Newman (5)
Waltham St Lawrence Primary School, West End

Alexandra's First Riddle

What could it be?
Follow the clues and see.

It looks **like a fish.**
It sounds **like a rainbow.**
It smells **like a strawberry.**
It feels **like a fish.**
It tastes **like a strawberry.**

Have you guessed what it could be?
Look below and you will see,
It is...

Answer: **A mermaid.**

Alexandra "Lexy" Elizabeth Barden Gleave (5)
Waltham St Lawrence Primary School, West End

Tejas' First Riddle

What could it be?
Follow the clues and see.

It looks **yellow**.
It sounds **quiet**.
It smells **like a milkshake**.
It feels **soft**.
It tastes **yummy**.

Have you guessed what it could be?
Look below and you will see,
It is...

Answer: **A banana.**

Tejas Dholiwar (5)
Waltham St Lawrence Primary School, West End

Effie's First Riddle

What could it be?
Follow the clues and see.

It looks **colourful and bright, but you can't see it at night.**
It sounds **like nothing to hear, but you can see it from far or near.**
It smells **like the rain and the sun, mix them together, they make something fun.**
It feels **like something we can't touch, although I would like to very much.**
It tastes **like... Skittles.**

Have you guessed what it could be?
Look below and you will see,
It is...

Answer: **A rainbow.**

Effie Schofield (5)
West Heath Primary School, West Heath

Lashea's First Riddle

What could it be?
Follow the clues and see.

It looks **long, round and green.**
It sounds **crunchy.**
It smells **yummy and tasty.**
It feels **hard when it's in your hand. Once cut, crunchy, slippery and slimy.**
It tastes **juicy, soft and crunchy.**

Have you guessed what it could be?
Look below and you will see,
It is...

Answer: **A cucumber.**

Lashea Shiv Zimmerman (5)
West Heath Primary School, West Heath

Megan's First Riddle

What could it be?
Follow the clues and see.

It looks **bouncy, wobbly and red.**
It sounds **wobbly**.
It smells **like fruit.**
It feels **springy**.
It tastes **like fruit - a strawberry.**

Have you guessed what it could be?
Look below and you will see,
It is...

Answer: Strawberry jelly.

Megan Ringham (5)
West Heath Primary School, West Heath

Laila-Rose's First Riddle

What could it be?
Follow the clues and see.

It looks **spotted and red**.
It sounds **like January**.
It smells **sweet**.
It feels **wet and juicy**.
It tastes **delicious**.

Have you guessed what it could be?
Look below and you will see,
It is...

Answer: **A strawberry**.

Laila-Rose Kinahan (5)
West Heath Primary School, West Heath

Willow's First Riddle

What could it be?
Follow the clues and see.

It looks **white**.
It sounds **squeaky**.
It smells **cheesy**.
It feels **squishy**.
It tastes **salty**.

Have you guessed what it could be?
Look below and you will see,
It is...

Answer: **Halloumi.**

Willow Ford (5)
West Heath Primary School, West Heath

Charlie's First Riddle

What could it be?
Follow the clues and see.

It looks **oval**.
It sounds **like a crack**.
It smells **lovely**.
It feels **hard**.
It tastes **yummy**.

Have you guessed what it could be?
Look below and you will see,
It is...

Answer: **An egg**.

Charlie Skinner (5)
West Heath Primary School, West Heath

Ronnie's First Riddle

What could it be?
Follow the clues and see.

It looks **round**.
It sounds **bouncy**.
It smells **rubbery**.
It feels **squidgy**.
It tastes **yucky**.

Have you guessed what it could be?
Look below and you will see,
It is...

Answer: **A ball.**

Ronnie Marshall (4)
West Heath Primary School, West Heath

Florence's First Riddle

What could it be?
Follow the clues and see.

It looks **round and small.**
It smells **sweet and like chocolate**.
It feels **soft**.
It tastes **yummy**.

Have you guessed what it could be?
Look below and you will see,
It is...

Answer: **A cupcake.**

Florence Ball (5)
West Heath Primary School, West Heath

Aarav's First Riddle

This is my riddle about an amazing animal.
What could it be?
Follow the clues to see!

This animal has **a shell** on its body,
And its colour is **green and yellow.**
This animal has **four** feet,
It likes **grass and crabs** to eat.
The seaside is where it lives,
Its favourite thing to do is **swim.**
This animal has **two long** ears,
It makes **'eeeeeeeeeeeweeeeee!'** sounds
for you to hear.

Are you an animal whizz?
Have you guessed what it is?
It is...

Answer: **A turtle.**

Aarav Sheth (5)
Wimbledon Common Preparatory School,
Wimbledon

Freddy's First Riddle

This is my riddle about an amazing animal.
What could it be?
Follow the clues to see!

This animal has **scales** on its body,
And its colour is **shiny and green**.
This animal has **no** feet,
It likes **people and animals** to eat.
A jungle is where it lives,
Its favourite thing to do is **slither**.
This animal has **no** ears,
It makes **'hiss, hiss!'** sounds for you to hear.

Are you an animal whizz?
Have you guessed what it is?
It is...

Answer: **A python.**

Freddy Casey (5)
Wimbledon Common Preparatory School,
Wimbledon

Michael's First Riddle

This is my riddle about an amazing animal.
What could it be?
Follow the clues to see!

This animal has **scales** on its body,
And its colour is **dark and a little bit red**.
This animal has **six** feet,
It likes **people** to eat.
In the sand is where it lives,
Its favourite thing to do is **stay out in the sun**.
This animal has **six** ears,
It makes **a cracking** sound for you to hear.

Are you an animal whizz?
Have you guessed what it is?
It is...

Answer: **A scorpion.**

Michael Kok Coustar (5)
Wimbledon Common Preparatory School,
Wimbledon

Matthew's First Riddle

This is my riddle about an amazing animal.
What could it be?
Follow the clues to see!

This animal has **feathers** on its body,
And its colour is **green**.
This animal has **two** feet,
It likes **worms** to eat.
The rainforest is where it lives,
Its favourite thing to do is **show its feathers**.
This animal has **two** ears,
It makes **screeching** sounds for you to hear.

Are you an animal whizz?
Have you guessed what it is?
It is...

Answer: **A peacock.**

Matthew Cook (5)
Wimbledon Common Preparatory School,
Wimbledon

Nikolai's First Riddle

This is my riddle about an amazing animal.
What could it be?
Follow the clues to see!

This animal has **stripes** on its body,
And its colour is **black and white**.
This animal has **four** feet,
It likes **grass** to eat.
Near some trees is where it lives,
Its favourite thing to do is **munch grass**.
This animal has **two** ears,
It makes **quiet** sounds for you to hear.

Are you an animal whizz?
Have you guessed what it is?
It is...

Answer: **A zebra**.

Nikolai Gosling (5)
Wimbledon Common Preparatory School,
Wimbledon

James' First Riddle

This is my riddle about an amazing animal.
What could it be?
Follow the clues to see!

This animal has **scales** on its body,
And its colour is **green and grey**.
This animal has **four** feet,
It likes **people and animals** to eat.
Australia is where it lives,
Its favourite thing to do is **swim**.
This animal has **two** ears,
It makes **snap, snap** sounds for you to hear.

Are you an animal whizz?
Have you guessed what it is?
It is...

Answer: **A crocodile.**

James Michael Haywood (5)
Wimbledon Common Preparatory School,
Wimbledon

Noah's First Riddle

This is my riddle about an amazing animal.
What could it be?
Follow the clues to see!

This animal has **two wings** on its body,
And its colour is **black and yellow.**
This animal has **six** feet,
It likes **nectar** to eat.
A hive is where it lives,
Its favourite thing to do is **make honey.**
This animal has **two** ears,
It makes **buzzing** sounds for you to hear.

Are you an animal whizz?
Have you guessed what it is?
It is...

Answer: **A bee.**

Noah Thomas (5)
Wimbledon Common Preparatory School,
Wimbledon

Misha's First Riddle

This is my riddle about an amazing animal.
What could it be?
Follow the clues to see!

This animal has **hair** on its body,
And its colour is **orange**.
This animal has **four** feet,
It likes **pet food** to eat.
In my house is where it lives,
Its favourite thing to do is **play with me**.
This animal has **two** ears,
It makes **woofing** sounds for you to hear.

Are you an animal whizz?
Have you guessed what it is?
It is...

Answer: **A dog.**

Misha Kutsenko (5)
Wimbledon Common Preparatory School,
Wimbledon

Elias' First Riddle

This is my riddle about an amazing animal.
What could it be?
Follow the clues to see!

This animal has **green scales** on its body,
And its colour is **sparkly**.
This animal has **six** feet,
It likes **flies** to eat.
In the grass is where it lives,
Its favourite thing to do is **jump**.
This animal has **two** ears,
It makes **buzzing** sounds for you to hear.

Are you an animal whizz?
Have you guessed what it is?
It is...

Answer: **A grasshopper**.

Elias Tobler Borsting (5)
Wimbledon Common Preparatory School,
Wimbledon

Johnathan's First Riddle

This is my riddle about an amazing animal.
What could it be?
Follow the clues to see!

This animal has **a shell** on its body,
And its colour is **black and red**.
This animal has **six** feet,
It likes **leaves** to eat.
The grass is where it lives,
Its favourite thing to do is **fly around**.
This animal has **no** ears,
It makes **no** sounds for you to hear.

Are you an animal whizz?
Have you guessed what it is?
It is...

Answer: **A ladybird**.

Johnathan Paice (5)
Wimbledon Common Preparatory School,
Wimbledon

Nathan's First Riddle

This is my riddle about an amazing animal.
What could it be?
Follow the clues to see!

This animal has **soft fur** on its body,
And its colour is **yellow**.
This animal has **four** feet,
It likes **beef** to eat.
In a cave is where it lives,
Its favourite thing to do is **roar**.
This animal has **two** ears,
It makes **loud** sounds for you to hear.

Are you an animal whizz?
Have you guessed what it is?
It is...

Answer: **A lion.**

Nathan Zhang (5)
Wimbledon Common Preparatory School,
Wimbledon

David's First Riddle

This is my super first riddle.
What could it be?
Follow the clues to see!

On the ground is where you'll find it,
It's made out of **three body parts**.
It is used for **helping each other**,
Its colour is **black or red**.
It is a **very small** shape,
It has **a strong body and legs**.

Have you guessed what it could be?
Look below and you will see,
It is...

Answer: **An ant.**

David Jeens (5)
Wimbledon Common Preparatory School,
Wimbledon

Frederick's First Riddle

This is my super first riddle.
What could it be?
Follow the clues to see!

Under a rock is where you'll find it,
It's made out of **legs and a thorax.**
It is used for **catching mosquitos**,
Its colour is **red and black.**
It is a **circle** shape,
It has **sharp fangs.**

Have you guessed what it could be?
Look below and you will see,
It is...

Answer: **A spider.**

Frederick Rossen (5)
Wimbledon Common Preparatory School, Wimbledon

Hugo's First Riddle

This is my super first riddle.
What could it be?
Follow the clues to see!

In a nest is where you'll find it,
It's made out of **wings and a sting**.
It is used for **eating bees heads**,
Its colour is **yellow and black**.
It is a **round oval** shape,
It stings you.

Have you guessed what it could be?
Look below and you will see,
It is...

Answer: **A hornet**.

Hugo Stehn (5)
Wimbledon Common Preparatory School,
Wimbledon

My First Riddle

This is my super first riddle.
What could it be?
Follow the clues to see!

In the zoo is where you'll find it,
It's made out of **fur**.
It is used **for catching food**,
Its colour is **black and orange**.
It is a **lion** shape,
It has **black stripes**.

Have you guessed what it could be?
Look below and you will see,
It is...

Answer: **A tiger.**

L Kee (4)

Wimbledon Common Preparatory School,
Wimbledon

Edward's First Riddle

This is my super first riddle.
What could it be?
Follow the clues to see!

In a nest is where you'll find it,
It's made out of **wings**.
It is used for **eating bees**,
Its colour is **yellow and black**.
It is an **oval** shape,
It has **a sting so it can sting you**.

Have you guessed what it could be?
Look below and you will see,
It is...

Answer: **A hornet.**

Edward Gleave (5)
Wimbledon Common Preparatory School,
Wimbledon

Henry's First Riddle

This is my super first riddle.
What could it be?
Follow the clues to see!

On a plant is where you'll find it,
It's made out of **legs and wings.**
It is used for **eating aphids**,
Its colour is **red and black.**
It is a **circular** shape,
It has **black spots**.

Have you guessed what it could be?
Look below and you will see,
It is...

Answer: **A ladybird.**

Henry Michalski (4)
Wimbledon Common Preparatory School,
Wimbledon

Vihaan's First Riddle

This is my super first riddle.
What could it be?
Follow the clues to see!

In the ground is where you'll find it,
It's made out of **a long body**.
It is used for **looking after the soil**,
Its colour is **peach**.
It is a **cylinder** shape,
It has **one whole body**.

Have you guessed what it could be?
Look below and you will see,
It is...

Answer: **A worm.**

Vihaan Narula (5)
Wimbledon Common Preparatory School, Wimbledon

Jake's First Riddle

This is my super first riddle.
What could it be?
Follow the clues to see!

In a web is where you'll find it,
It's made out of **four fangs.**
It is used for **eating flies,**
Its colour is **black and red.**
It is a **circle and oval** shape,
It has **eight legs.**

Have you guessed what it could be?
Look below and you will see,
It is...

Answer: **A spider.**

Jake Collins (5)
Wimbledon Common Preparatory School,
Wimbledon

Pedro's First Riddle

This is my super first riddle.
What could it be?
Follow the clues to see!

In a web is where you'll find it,
It's made out of **fur and legs**.
It is used for **making a web**,
Its colour is **black and orange**.
It is a **circle** shape,
It has **eight legs**.

Have you guessed what it could be?
Look below and you will see,
It is...

Answer: **A tarantula**.

Pedro Borges Lima (5)
Wimbledon Common Preparatory School,
Wimbledon

Vincent's First Riddle

This is my super first riddle.
What could it be?
Follow the clues to see!

In the jungle is where you'll find it,
It's made out of **fur**.
It is used for **catching food**,
Its colour is **light brown**.
It is a **tiger** shape,
It has **sharp teeth and a mane**.

Have you guessed what it could be?
Look below and you will see,
It is...

Answer: **A lion.**

Vincent Loganathan (5)
Wimbledon Common Preparatory School,
Wimbledon

Max's First Riddle

This is my super first riddle.
What could it be?
Follow the clues to see!

In the lake is where you'll find it,
It's made out of **hard skin**.
It is used for **catching food**,
Its colour is **green**.
It is a **long and thin** shape,
It has **sharp teeth**.

Have you guessed what it could be?
Look below and you will see,
It is...

Answer: **A crocodile.**

Max Lowe (4)
Wimbledon Common Preparatory School,
Wimbledon

Joshua's First Riddle

This is my super first riddle.
What could it be?
Follow the clues to see!

In grass is where you'll find it,
It's made out of **wings and legs**.
It is used for **eating grass**,
Its colour is **green and brown**.
It is an **oval** shape,
It has **wings**.

Have you guessed what it could be?
Look below and you will see,
It is...

Answer: **A grasshopper.**

Joshua Howard (5)
Wimbledon Common Preparatory School,
Wimbledon

Kabir's First Riddle

This is my super first riddle.
What could it be?
Follow the clues to see!

In the water is where you'll find it,
It's made out of **metal**.
It is used for **playing with**,
Its colour is **red, blue and yellow**.
It is an **oval** shape,
It has **a jet engine**.

Have you guessed what it could be?
Look below and you will see,
It is...

Answer: **A boat.**

Kabir Malik (5)
Wimbledon Common Preparatory School,
Wimbledon

Atlas' First Riddle

This is my super first riddle.
What could it be?
Follow the clues to see!

In the wild is where you'll find it,
It's made out of **fur and skin.**
It is used for **fighting,**
Its colour is **black and yellow.**
It is a **cat** shape,
It has **sharp claws.**

Have you guessed what it could be?
Look below and you will see,
It is...

Answer: **A jaguar.**

Atlas Aydin (5)
Wimbledon Common Preparatory School,
Wimbledon

Arlo's First Riddle

This is my super first riddle.
What could it be?
Follow the clues to see!

In a pond is where you'll find it,
It's made out of **wings and antennae**.
It is used for **flying**,
Its colour is **green**.
It is an **oval** shape,
It has **shiny wings**.

Have you guessed what it could be?
Look below and you will see,
It is...

Answer: **A dragonfly.**

Arlo Mumford (5)
Wimbledon Common Preparatory School,
Wimbledon

Samuel's First Riddle

This is my super first riddle.
What could it be?
Follow the clues to see!

In a nest is where you'll find it,
It's made out of **wings**.
It is used for **eating insects and bees**,
Its colour is **yellow**.
It is an **oval** shape,
It can sting you.

Have you guessed what it could be?
Look below and you will see,
It is...

Answer: **A hornet**.

Samuel Squelch (5)

Wimbledon Common Preparatory School,
Wimbledon

Hawken's First Riddle

This is my super first riddle.
What could it be?
Follow the clues to see!

In the grasslands is where you'll find it,
It's made out of **fur**.
It is used for **running fast**,
Its colour is **yellow and brown.**
It is a **cat** shape,
It has **spots**.

Have you guessed what it could be?
Look below and you will see,
It is...

Answer: **A cheetah.**

Hawken Edwards (5)
Wimbledon Common Preparatory School,
Wimbledon

Nicholas' First Riddle

This is my super first riddle.
What could it be?
Follow the clues to see!

In the jungle is where you'll find it,
It's made out of **skin and fur**.
It is used for **biting**,
Its colour is **yellow and brown**.
It is a **cat** shape,
It has **a mane**.

Have you guessed what it could be?
Look below and you will see,
It is...

Answer: **A lion.**

Nicholas Harries (5)
Wimbledon Common Preparatory School,
Wimbledon

Zayne's First Riddle

This is my super first riddle.
What could it be?
Follow the clues to see!

In the soil is where you'll find it,
It's made out of **a head**.
It is used for **eating the soil**,
Its colour is **pink**.
It is an **oval** shape,
It has **no legs**.

Have you guessed what it could be?
Look below and you will see,
It is...

Answer: **A worm.**

Zayne Ali (5)
Wimbledon Common Preparatory School,
Wimbledon

Jack's First Riddle

This is my super first riddle.
What could it be?
Follow the clues to see!

In Asia is where you'll find it,
It's made out of **skin**.
It is used for **spraying plants**,
Its colour is **grey**.
It is a **big** shape,
It has **two tusks**.

Have you guessed what it could be?
Look below and you will see,
It is...

Answer: **An elephant.**

Jack Doran (5)
Wimbledon Common Preparatory School,
Wimbledon

Arwen's First Riddle

What could it be?
Follow the clues and see.

It looks **stripy and pretty.**
It sounds **crunchy.**
It smells **like the sea.**
It feels **hard, rough and smooth.**
It tastes **salty.**

Have you guessed what it could be?
Look below and you will see,
It is...

Answer: **A seashell.**

Arwen Rose Peralta Camanan (5)
Ysgol Parcyrhun, Ammanford

Parthan's First Riddle

What could it be?
Follow the clues and see.

It looks **like a king's castle.**
It sounds **like the sea.**
It smells **like wet sand.**
It feels **soft.**
It tastes **salty.**

Have you guessed what it could be?
Look below and you will see,
It is...

Answer: **A sandcastle.**

Parthan Mohan (5)
Ysgol Parcyrhun, Ammanford

YOUNG WRITERS INFORMATION

We hope you have enjoyed reading this book – and that you will continue to in the coming years.

If you're a young writer who enjoys reading and creative writing, or the parent of an enthusiastic poet or story writer, do visit our website **www.youngwriters.co.uk**. Here you will find free competitions, workshops and games, as well as recommended reads, a poetry glossary and our blog. There's lots to keep budding writers motivated to write!

If you would like to order further copies of this book, or any of our other titles, then please give us a call or order via your online account.

Young Writers
Remus House
Coltsfoot Drive
Peterborough
PE2 9BF
(01733) 890066
info@youngwriters.co.uk

Join in the conversation!
Tips, news, giveaways and much more!